THE Twelve
Days of Christmas

THE Twelve

For Lia

Illustrated by JAN BRETT

Days of
Christmas

SIMON & SCHUSTER

LONDON • SYDNEY • NEW YORK • TOKYO • SINGAPORE • TORONTO

THE TWELVE DAYS

English traditional carol

VERSES 1-4

1. On the first* day of Christ-mas my
2. On the se-cond* day of Christ-mas my

true love gave to me a
true love gave to me

four col-ly birds, three French hens, two tur-tle-doves, and a par-tridge in a pear tree.
four three two

VERSES 5-12

5. On the fifth* day of Christ-mas my true love gave to me twelve lords a-leap-ing,
6. On the sixth* day of Christ-mas my true love gave to me twelve

*Sing appropriate number of day, and then cut from † to appropriate boxed number.

OF CHRISTMAS

e-lev'n la-dies danc-ing, ten pi-pers pi-ping,
e-lev'n ten

nine drum-mers drum-ming, eight maids a-milk-ing,
nine eight

sev'n swans a-swim-ming, six geese a-lay-ing, five gold rings, four___ col-ly birds,
sev'n six five gold rings four___ col-ly birds,

three French hens, two___ tur-tle-doves, and a par-tridge___ in a pear tree.

On the first day of Christmas

My true love gave to me
A partridge in a pear tree.

On the second day of Christmas
My true love gave to me

Two turtledoves,
And a partridge in a pear tree.

On the third day of Christmas
My true love gave to me
Three French hens,

Two turtledoves,
And a partridge in a pear tree.

On the fourth day of Christmas
My true love gave to me
Four colly birds,

Three French hens,
Two turtledoves,
And a partridge in a pear tree.

On the fifth day of Christmas
My true love gave to me
Five gold rings,
Four colly birds,

Three French hens,
Two turtledoves,
And a partridge in a pear tree.

© KERSTDAGEN

On the sixth day of Christmas
My true love gave to me
Six geese a-laying,
Five gold rings,

Four colly birds,
Three French hens,
Two turtledoves,
And a partridge in a pear tree.

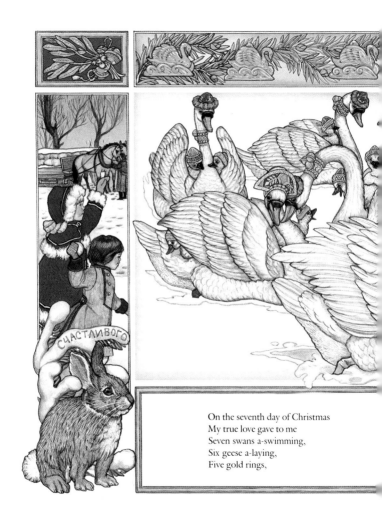

On the seventh day of Christmas
My true love gave to me
Seven swans a-swimming,
Six geese a-laying,
Five gold rings,

Four colly birds,
Three French hens,
Two turtledoves,
And a partridge in a pear tree.

РОЖДЕСТВА!

On the eighth day of Christmas
My true love gave to me
Eight maids a-milking,
Seven swans a-swimming,
Six geese a-laying,

Five gold rings,
Four colly birds,
Three French hens,
Two turtledoves,
And a partridge in a pear tree.

On the ninth day of Christmas
My true love gave to me
Nine drummers drumming,
Eight maids a-milking,
Seven swans a-swimming,
Six geese a-laying,

Five gold rings,
Four colly birds,
Three French hens,
Two turtledoves,
And a partridge in a pear tree.

On the tenth day of Christmas
My true love gave to me
Ten pipers piping,
Nine drummers drumming,
Eight maids a-milking,
Seven swans a-swimming,

Six geese a-laying,
Five gold rings,
Four colly birds,
Three French hens,
Two turtledoves,
And a partridge in a pear tree.

Chridheil

On the eleventh day of Christmas
My true love gave to me
Eleven ladies dancing,
Ten pipers piping,
Nine drummers drumming,
Eight maids a-milking,
Seven swans a-swimming,

Six geese a-laying,
Five gold rings,
Four colly birds,
Three French hens,
Two turtledoves,
And a partridge in a pear tree.

On the twelfth day of Christmas
My true love gave to me
Twelve lords a-leaping,
Eleven ladies dancing,
Ten pipers piping,
Nine drummers drumming,
Eight maids a-milking,

Seven swans a-swimming,
Six geese a-laying,
Five gold rings,
Four colly birds,
Three French hens,
Two turtledoves,
And a partridge in a pear tree.

New Year!

First published in Great Britain in large format
in 1987 by Macdonald & Co. (Publishers) Ltd.
This edition first published in Great Britain
in 1990 by Simon & Schuster Young Books, Wolsey
House, Wolsey Road, Hemel Hempstead HP2 4SS.
Original American edition published in 1986 by
Dodd, Mead & Company, Inc., New York, New York, USA.
Illustrations copyright © 1986 by Jan Brett Studio, Inc
All rights reserved, including the right of reproduction
in whole or in part in any form. Published by arrangement
with G. P. Putnam's Sons, a division of the Putnam & Grosset
Book Group. Printed in Singapore by Tien Wah Press (Pte) Ltd.
Music adapted from *CAROLS FOR CHRISTMAS*, compiled
and arranged by David Willcocks. Copyright © 1983 by
The Metropolitan Museum of Art. Reprinted by
permission of Henry Holt and Company, Inc.